*for Scott and Bruce*

# TOMMY'S SCOTTISH TUNES

Catchy, well known tunes for the young music maker to enjoy. Words to the tunes are also given so that family or friends can sing along.

Although written for violinists this book can also be used by other young instrumentalists or singers.

Have fun with Tommy's Quiz, his Memory Tune and, of course, Tommy's Own Tune – and, if you want to, colour in the drawings as well!

Chosen and adapted by Joyce McIver
Drawings by Andrew Magee

Dear Young Music Maker,

Hello, I'm very pleased to meet you!

My name is Tommy McTavish and I come from Falkland, a wee village in Fife, in the east of Scotland.

I just love to play and sing my tunes. Sometimes I play and my friends sing. Sometimes I play and my family sing.

Sometimes I practise very hard on my own! But I always have great fun!

I hope *you* have great fun learning all my Scottish tunes!

Look out for my paw prints – they might help you! Happy playing and happy singing! Lots of love,

Tommy

## CONTENTS

Here is my very own tune - I hope you like it!  You can play it or sing it as a round.
Start each part at my paw print.

# Tommy's Own Tune

*Joyce McIver*

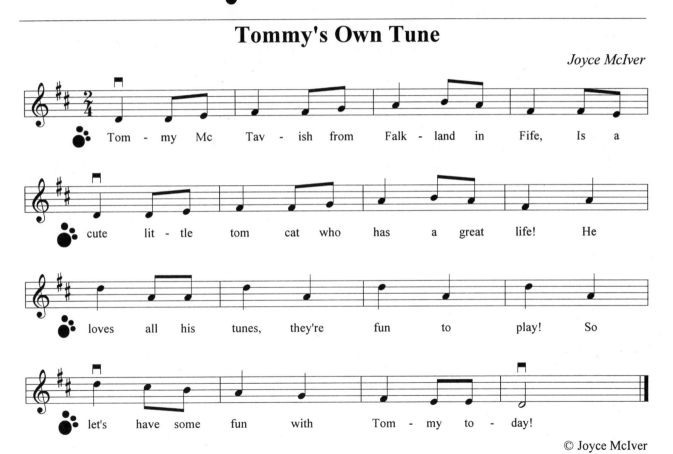

Tommy says "If you can, with your pencil please, carefully name the notes of this tune. Start at my single paw mark." 

## Tune 1

# Coulter's Candy

*Traditional*

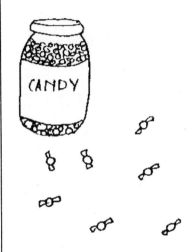

Ally, bally, ally bally bee,
Sittin' on yer mammy's knee,
*Greetin'* for anither *bawbee*,
Tae buy mair Coulter's Candy

Ally, bally, ally bally bee,
When you grow up you'll go to sea,
Makin' pennies for your daddy and me,
Tae buy mair Coulter's candy.

*Repeat verse 1*

*Greetin': crying. bawbee: small coin, penny*

Tommy's Tip for violinists, "Take care with the two up bows" ( ⌄ ⌄ )

## Tune 2

# Three Craws

*Traditional*

Three craws sat upon a wa'
Sat upon a wa', sat upon a wa',
Three craws sat upon a wa'
On a cold and frosty morning.

The first craw couldnae *flee* at a,
Couldnae flee at a', couldnae flee at a',
The first craw couldnae flee at a,
On a cold and frosty morning.

The second craw fell and broke his jaw
Fell and broke his jaw, fell and broke his jaw
The second craw fell and broke his jaw
On a cold and frosty morning.

The third craw was *greetin'* for his maw,
Greetin' for his maw, greetin' for his maw
The third craw was greetin' for his maw,
On a cold and frosty morning.

The fourth craw wasnae there at a' _ _ _ _ _ _

*Flee: fly    greetin': crying*

## Tune 3        The Hundred Pipers

*Traditional*

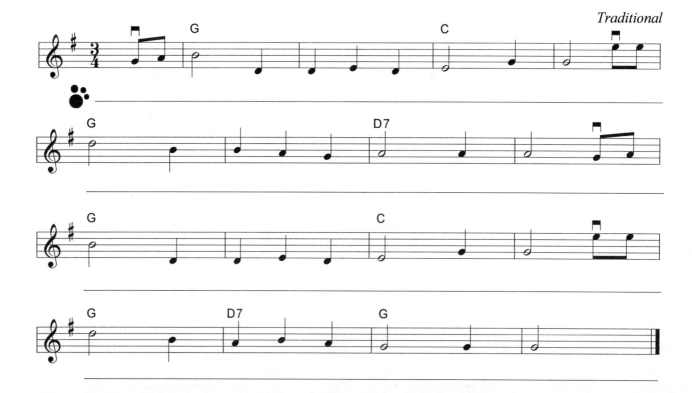

Wi' a hundred pipers an' *a'* an' a',
Wi' a hundred pipers an' a' an' a',
We'll up an' gie them a blaw, a blaw,
Wi' a hundred pipers an' a' an' a'.

*a': all*

Tommy's Tip  "Watch out where there are six G notes in a row!"

## Tune 4       The Jeely Piece Song

*Adam McNaughtan*

Permission kindly granted by Adam McNaughtan

Oh, ye cannae fling *pieces* oot a twenty storey flat,
Seven hundred hungry *weans*'ll testify tae that.
If it's butter, cheese or *jeely*, if the *breid* is plain or pan,
The odds against it reaching earth are ninety-nine tae wan.


*pieces: sandwiches*
*weans: children*
*jeely: jam*
*breid: bread*

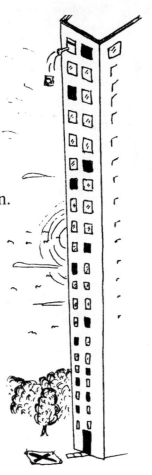

## Tune 5

# I Love a Lassie

*Words:  Harry Lauder*
*and Gerald Grafton*
*Music: Harry Lauder*

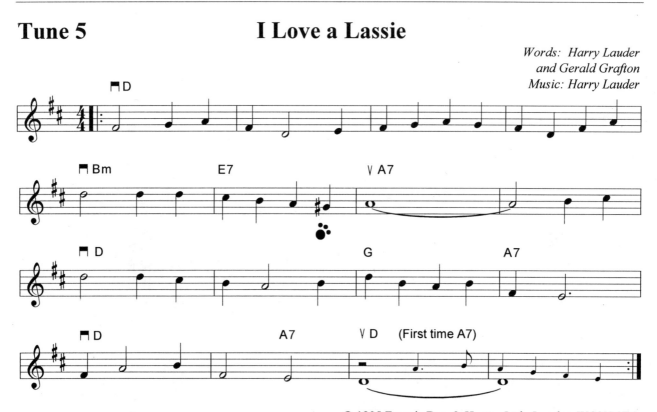

I love a lassie,
A bonnie, bonnie lassie,
She's as pure as the lily in the dell.
She's as sweet as the heather,
The bonnie, bloomin' heather,
Mary, ma Scotch Bluebell!

*(sing twice)*

Tommy's Tip for violinists "Use slow bows for the long tied notes (and watch out for all the C♮ and F♮ s)"

# Tune 6

# Flower of Scotland

*Roy Williamson*

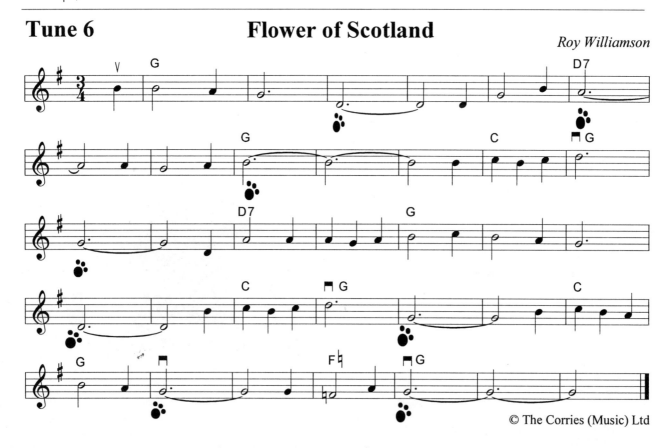

O flower of Scotland,
When will we see
Your like again?
That fought and died for
Your wee bit hill and glen
And stood against him
Proud Edward's army
And sent him homeward
Tae think again.

# Tune 7      **Ye Canny Shove Yer Granny**

*Traditional*

Oh ye canny shove yer Granny aff a bus,
Oh ye canny shove yer Granny aff a bus,
Oh ye canny shove yer Granny, for she's yer Mammy's Mammy,
Oh ye canny shove yer Granny aff a bus.

# Tune 8

# Mairi's Wedding

*Words: Hugh S Roberton*
*Traditional*

Step we gaily, on we go,
Heel for heel and toe for toe,
Arm in arm and row on row,
All for Mairi's wedding.

Over hillways up and down,
Myrtle green and bracken brown,
Past the *shielings*, thro' the town,
All for sake o'Mairi.

Step we gaily, etc

*shieling: a summer pasture on the hillside with a rough hut*
*to shelter shepherds, etc*

Tommy asks "Have you heard of the Beatles?  One of them, Paul McCartney, wrote the music for this tune.  Have *you* seen the mist rolling in from the sea anywhere?"

## Tune 9                    Mull of Kintyre

*McCartney-Laine*

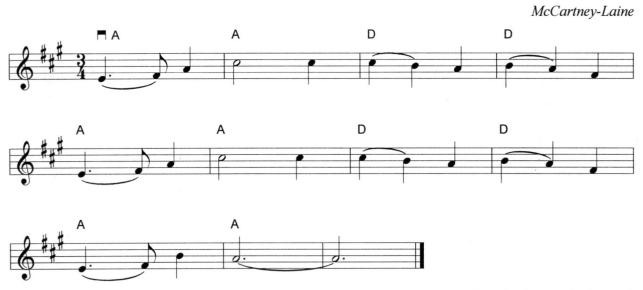

"Here is my Memory Tune. This means I can play it without looking at the music. Carefully learn the tune and see if you can play or sing it by memory. Good Luck and keep trying!"     Tommy

Mull of Kintyre,
Oh mist rolling in from
The sea, my desire
Is always to be here,
Oh Mull of Kintyre.

I played this tune by memory today!   (date) _____

Tommy's Tip "Make this tune sound as beautiful as you can - Loch Lomond is very beautiful."

# Tune 10     **Loch Lomond**

*Traditional*

By yon bonnie banks and by yon bonny *braes*,
Where the sun shines bright on Loch Lomond,
Where me and my true love spent *mony* happy days
On the bonnie, bonnie banks o' Loch Lomond.

Oh, ye'll tak' the high road and I'll tak' the low road,
An' I'll be in Scotland *afore* ye;
But me and my true love will never meet again,
On the bonnie, bonnie banks o' Loch Lomond.

*braes: hills     mony: many     afore: before*

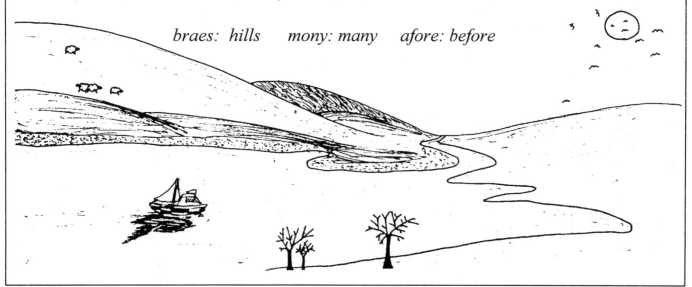

# Tommy's Quiz

Tommy wonders what you've discovered about the music and the tunes in this book. Check with your teacher if you've got all the answers right.  Good Luck!

1.  What is the name of the Loch with "bonnie banks and braes"? _____

2.  ‖: What does this sign mean? _____

3.  How many "pipers" were there?

4.  How many tunes have one sharp (#) in the key signature?  Can you name the key? ____

5.  What happened to the second craw? _____

6.  𝄞 What is this sign called? _____

7.  Where did they dance "arm in arm" with heels and toes? _____

8.  How many tunes have two beats in each bar?  ( $\frac{2}{4}$ time) _____

9.  What is wrong with the building in The Jeely Piece Song? _____

10. Which tune is the Memory Tune?  Can you play it by memory yet? _____

"Well done!  See you soon."           Love,  Tommy